mgb

Published by Mirror Group Books,
79 Camden Road, London, NW1 9NT.
Printed and bound in England by
Hazell Watson & Viney Ltd,
Aylesbury, Bucks.

ISBN 0 85939 057 8

A MIRROR GROUP BOOK

laugh again with

ANDY CAPP

No.15

CARTOONS BY REG SMYTHE

C'MON, KID

WHAT'S THAT FOR?

FOR ASKIN' ME OUT WHEN I'M BROKE
MONEY ISN'T EVERYTHIN', Y'KNOW

PAWNBROKER
-THERE'S YER WRISTWATCH, THERE'S YER-

YAWN

DON'T BOTHER SEARCHIN' FOR THE LIGHT SWITCH — THEY'VE CUT OFF THE ELECTRICITY!

D'YER EVER 'AVE ANY GOOD NEWS?!
YES! THERE'LL BE LESS THINGS F' YER T' BUMP INTO — THEY'VE RE-POSSESSED THE SUITE!

ASK A SILLY QUESTION—

EMPLOYMENT EXCHANGE
HEY, ANDY! ARE YER INTERESTED IN THE CHANCE OF A LIFETIME—?!

A RESPONSIBLE JOB, TOP MONEY, NO AGE LIMIT, JUST A DESIRE TO SUCCEED—!

I DON'T THINK SO, HARRY, THANKS ALL THE SAME

AT MY TIME O' LIFE IT'S TOO BIG A JUMP FROM FRAYED CUFFS T' FRAYED NERVES!

?

DOES SHE KISS YER LIKE THAT EVERY TIME YER COME OUT, ERIC?

AS A MATTER OF FACT, SHE DOES

DON'T YER MIND?
Smythe

CAN YER SPARE 'ER TOMORROW NIGHT, GAFFER? I'D LIKE TO TAKE 'ER TO THE CLUB DANCE

'AVE YER SEEN ME MISSUS?

SURE, BUT I'D STILL PREFER T' TAKE YER BARMAID! HEH! HEH!
ME TOO

BOP!

IT WAS AN ACCIDENT, OFFICER —

I GOT IN FRONT OF ME MOTHER JUST AS 'E LET FLY

READ ANY GOOD BOOKS LATELY?

FLORRIE! AFTER ALL THESE YEARS!
DOROTHY!

TALK ABOUT YOUNG AN' FOOLISH! HEH! HEH! REMEMBER THAT DOUBLE DATE WE WENT ON?

HEH! HEH! YOU GOT LANDED WITH A RIGHT ONE! I BET THAT ROMANCE DIDN'T LAST VERY LONG!

YER RIGHT, DOT —I MARRIED 'IM

ALL RIGHT, LET'S 'EAR IT

1

I RAN INTO RAQUEL WELCH AN' I COULDN'T GET AWAY

2

HEH! HEH!
HEH! HEH! HEH! HEH!
HEH! HEH! HEH! HEH!
HEH! HEH!
3

WE BOTH 'AVE THE SAME SENSE OF HUMOUR – 'E *INSISTS!*
Smythe
4

BEEN AWAY, FLO?
YES, AMY, T' THE SEASIDE FOR A FEW DAYS

AN' I'LL BET YER'VE GOT THE HOTEL TOWELS T' PROVE IT! HEH! HEH!

THE SORT OF PLACES WE STAY, THE HOTEL PINCHES THE GUESTS' TOWELS
Smythe

SORRY ABOUT THE TIME, SWEET'EART – STILL LOVE ME?
OUT OF ME WAY, I'M LATE FOR WORK!

I'M SERIOUS, KID – 'OW D'YER RATE ME AS A 'USBAND?

IF I WAS ANY GOOD AT FRACTIONS I'D BE SAT BEHIND A DESK, NOT ON ME KNEES SCRUBBIN' FLOORS!

'OW DID 'E GET ON ABOUT 'IS STOMACH, FLORRIE?
'E'S TAKIN' IT VERY 'ARD, CHALKIE –

THE DOCTOR SAID T' CUT OUT THE BOOZE – 'E'S JUST ALLOWED TO 'AVE A PINT AT MEALTIMES

'OW ARE YER FEELIN' ANDY?

'OW WOULD YOU FEEL IF YER WERE EATIN' SIXTEEN MEALS A DAY?!
Smythe

SEE YER LATER – I'VE JUST 'EARD THAT JERRY 'ARRIS 'AS BEEN TAKEN TO 'OSPITAL WITH A BROKEN LEG!

JUST GOES T' SHOW – 'E CAN BE SOFT-'EARTED WHEN 'E LIKES

BLIMEY! I'M NOT THE ONLY ONE WITH AN EYE ON 'IS CUP FINAL TICKET!

CITIZENS
ADVICE
BUREAU
GET THE DRINKS IN, PET – I'LL JOIN YER SHORTLY

IF YOU 'AVE ANY PROBLEMS, I'M THE ONE YER SHOULD COME TO FIRST!

HUH! 'OW COULD YER 'AVE CONFIDENCE IN THE ADVICE OF ANYBODY WHO WOULD MARRY ME?
Smythe

MOTHER'S JUST THIS MINUTE LEFT, PET, GIVE 'ER A WAVE

WHOSE MOTHER?
MY MOTHER

WITH PLEASURE

Smythe

I'VE GOT THE SACK, ANDY —I'VE BEEN TOLD T' PICK UP ME CARDS AT CLOSIN' TIME!
OH, NO!

SWINE! 'AVE YOU ANY IDEA WHAT IT'S LIKE AT HIS AGE TO FIND ANOTHER GIRLFRIEND WHO'S WORKIN' ?!
SOB

WHAT'S UP, FLO? CAN'T YER SLEEP?
IF I DON'T FIND SOME MONEY, THEY'RE GOIN' T' TAKE THE FURNITURE AWAY TOMORROW! COULD YOU SLEEP?

TCH! IF YER DON'T TELL ME YER TROUBLES, 'OW CAN I 'ELP YER?

'ERE, GET A DROP O' THIS DOWN YER – THERE'S NOTHIN' LIKE IT FOR INSOMNIA!
RUM
Smythe

GIVE ME A LARGE SCOTCH, GAFFER, AN' 'AVE ONE YERSELF
?!
THANKS, MISS

HI! THERE, BEAUTIFUL!
LET'S GET OVER THERE, CHALKIE
HUH! I DON'T THINK MUCH OF THAT, LOOK AT 'ER LEGS —

LISTEN, STUPID, WHAT ARE WE AFTER — A SPENDER OR A FLIPPIN' SHOW JUMPER ?!

POOR LASS. C'MON, LAD, IT WOULDN'T 'URT YER...

GET YER COAT ON, KID, I'M TAKIN' YER OUT — AN' WE'LL DO WHAT YOU WANT T' DO. WHERE WOULD YOU LIKE TO SPEND THE EVENIN'?

I'M NOT FUSSY – JUST SOMEWHERE NEAR ME INCOME

I'M TRYIN' T' BE SERIOUS!
Smythe

YER DINNER'S RUINED! WHERE'VE YER BEEN? THE PUBS SHUT AN HOUR AGO!

I VISITED YER MOTHER
LIAR! I CAN CHECK, Y'KNOW! LET'S 'EAR MORE — 'OW WAS SHE?

ABOUT THE SAME — SHE WOULDN'T LET ME IN!

I BELIEVE YER — COME AN' SIT DOWN AN' I'LL OPEN A TIN
Smythe

BINGO

'OW DID YER GET ON, PET — ANY LUCK?

YEAH, ALL BAD. I 'AVEN'T EVEN GOT ME BUS FARE 'OME

BUS STOP
PUT THE KETTLE ON!

I'M JUST OFF
TO POST ME
POOLS, PET

IF YER WON THE
FIRST DIVIDEND
WOULD YER STILL
FEEL THE SAME
ABOUT ME?
HEH! HEH!

YEAH - I'D EVEN GO AS
FAR AS TO SAY
I'D MISS YER

OOO! SHE'S 'ARD!

BY THE WAY, THERE'S A CUP MATCH DOWN SOUTH ON SATURDAY, AN' I'LL BE STAYIN' OVERNIGHT. IT MEANS LEAVIN' YER ON YER OWN - WILL YER BE ALL RIGHT?

I'LL MANAGE

THREE WHOLE DAYS! — AN' YER SAID YER WERE ONLY STAYIN' OVERNIGHT!
1

2

3

GET YER COAT ON, KID, AN' I'LL TAKE YER OUT F' A DRINK —

— I'LL PAY YER BACK NEXT WEEK

YER HURTIN'
Smythe

COULD I HAVE A WORD WITH YOU, MR. CAPP?

ABOUT SUNDAY—
SUNDAY?

YES, SUNDAY. IF YOU MUST PUT BUTTONS IN THE COLLECTION PLATE, WOULD YOU MIND USING YOUR OWN, AND NOT THOSE FROM THE PEW SEATS?
Smythe

R.W.CLARK
M.D.
SURGERY
HOURS 6-

1

IT'S ME NERVES, DOCTOR. COULD YER GIMME SOMETHIN'?
PILLS AREN'T THE ANSWER, MRS. CAPP-

2

-I PREFER TO ATTACK THE ORIGIN OF THE TROUBLE

3

ALL RIGHT, MATE, GET 'EM UP -I'M READY WHEN YOU ARE!
Smythe

4

SORRY ABOUT HAVIN' TO CALL THE POLICE TO ANDY LAS' NIGHT, FLO — I 'OPE IT WON'T STOP 'IM COMIN' IN

IT *WILL*, MATE — YER TAKINGS ARE GOIN' T' TAKE A DIVE THIS WEEK

HEH! HEH! I'VE 'EARD 'IM SAY THAT BEFORE

THIS TIME THE *MAGISTRATE* SAID IT — SEVEN DAYS!

DID YER GET ME LETTER?
YEP
DEBT COLLECTOR

THEN WHY DIDN'T YER ANSWER IT?!
DEBT COLLECTOR

-BOP-
I PREFER TO ANSWER PEOPLE!

ALL THIS BECAUSE YER POOR WIFE WENT T' BINGO AN' YER'VE 'AD T' WAIT TEN MINUTES F' YER TEA?!

FORTY MINUTES!

TEN MINUTES!
NO, RUBE, FORTY -'E'S BEEN THUMPIN' ME FOR THIRTY

ALL RIGHT, CALL ME A LIAR-!

READY FOR BINGO, FLO?
SHE'S NOT GOIN'-SHE'S GOT A COLD

D'YER WANT ME T' KEEP YER COMPANY, FLO?
NO, SHE DOESN'T

WHEN DID YER LOSE YER VOICE, FLO?
ON ME WEDDIN' DAY, KID, ON ME WEDDIN' DAY!
Smythe

I'D BETTER BE RUNNING, MISTER CAPP, I'LL BE LATE F' ME DATE –

1

SHE'S PROMISED T' MARRY ME AN' I'VE GOT T' BE CAREFUL – YER KNOW 'OW WOMEN CAN CHANGE THEIR MINDS!
PROPAGANDA, SON –

2

'AVE YER EVER 'EARD OF A GROOM BEING LEFT WAITIN' AT THE CHURCH?
3

SAME AGAIN, GAFFER!
Smythe
4

BANG
BANG

BANG
BANG

FLIPPIN' MARVELLOUS! 'OW CAN YER REASON WITH A WOMAN WHO LOCKS YOU OUT BECAUSE YOU DON'T COME IN?!
Smythe

I'M BEGINNIN' T' THINK SERIOUSLY ABOUT EMIGRATIN'!

THIS UNEMPLOYMENT SITUATION REALLY 'AS ME WORRIED
?

IT 'AS?

IT 'AS! YOU SHOULD TRY FIGHTIN' FOR A BIT OF ELBOW ROOM IN THAT BETTIN' SHOP!
Smythe

BINGO
THE TIME!

EEK!

WIVES WHO SAY THEIR MEN DON'T LISTEN TO 'EM SHOULD JUST TRY USIN' THE SAME EXCUSE TWICE IN ONE WEEK!
Smythe

LOOK, I'LL MEET YER HALF WAY. I'M PREPARED T' FORGET HALF OF THAT THIRTY BOB YER OWE ME–

GREAT, TOM, GREAT – I'LL FORGET THE OTHER HALF!

ARE YER FEELIN' ALL RIGHT, TOM?
Smythe

TCH! TCH! DISGUSTIN'! —DON'T JUST STAND 'ERE AN' WATCH!

MIND YOU, SHE IS YER BEST BARMAID, AN' 'E IS YER BEST CUSTOMER...
3

BUSINESS IS BUSINESS
4

I'M GOIN' TO 'AVE A LOOK ROUND THE SHOPS — YER BIRTHDAY'S COMIN' UP SHORTLY
YER DON'T 'AVE T' BOTHER, PET

NOT ANOTHER WORD — I'M **GOIN'**!
ALL RIGHT, THEN...

...I 'OPE 'E DOESN'T CHOOSE ANYTHIN' I CAN'T AFFORD

I HEARD THAT REMARK!

HEY! YER'VE DROPPED SOMETHIN' – IS IT A LOVE LETTER? HEH! HEH!

I'LL SAY THIS F' YER, FLO – YER NEVER STOOP TO OPENIN' WHAT DOESN'T BELONG T' YER

YES, PET

IT'S THIS WEATHER – IF I BEND I CAN'T STRAIGHTEN UP AGAIN!

I SAW THIS IN THE SECOND-HAND SHOP, PET, AN' I THOUGHT IT WOULD BE JUST RIGHT FOR YER

DON'T YER THINK IT'S A BIT ON THE BIG SIDE, FLO?

OH, I WOULDN'T SAY THAT — A COUPLE OF FALLS IN THE CANAL AN' IT'LL BE PERFECT

YER RIGHT, KID — YER'VE GOT TO ALLOW F' SHRINKAGE

BOP

'E'S CARRYIN' TOO MUCH WEIGHT AS IT IS!

BLIMEY, IT TOOK YER LONG ENOUGH TO BEST 'ER, ANDY - YER MUST BE SLIPPIN'

IT'S GETTIN' TOUGH, CHALKIE - SHE'S A STONE HEAVIER EVERY YEAR!
Smythe

RAT-A-TAT
TAT-TAT!

WE DON'T NEED
NONE!

HOW DO YOU KNOW? I
COULD BE SELLING
ENGLISH LESSONS

THAT'S THE
TROUBLE WITH
ME – MY MOUTH
Smythe

BET YOU 'AD A TERRIBLE TIME WHEN ANDY CAME 'OME LAS'NIGHT, FLORRIE—

YER RIGHT — IT TOOK SIX OF 'IS MATES TO GET 'IM INTO THE HOUSE

SIX OF 'EM, EH? THEY MUST 'AVE BEEN A WEAK LOT!

NOT REALLY — I FOUGHT LIKE A TIGER
Smythe

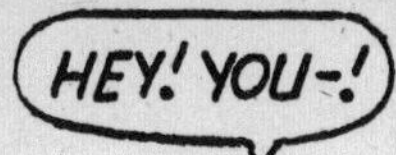
HEY! YOU-!

LOOK, ENA, DID WE OR DID WE NOT AGREE THAT I SHOULD 'AVE ONE NIGHT OUT A WEEK?
YE-ES...

WELL, THIS IS IT
BAR

I LIKE THIS BOY!
Smythe

1

2

EEK!
GRR! GRR!

3

HEY! FLO! COME AN' LOOK AT THIS WOMAN — SHE LOOKS SO MUCH LIKE YER MOTHER, IT'S UNCANNY!

4

WHAT A NIGHT I 'AD LAS' NIGHT, ANDY! HEH! HEH! THE BEER I SUPPED, AN' THE LITTLE DARLIN' I WALKED 'OME—!
HEH! HEH! YER A LAD, CHALKIE!

MEN! THEY'RE JUST LIKE KIDS —ALWAYS PRETENDIN' THEY DO THINGS THEY DON'T DO

NOT MY LITTLE DEVIL, RUBE —'E PRETENDS 'E ISN'T DOIN' THE THINGS 'E DOES DO!
Smythe

I WON'T BE LONG. I'M JUST OFF TO THE HAIRDRESSER'S

MMM.. LOVELY, KID — THAT STYLE REALLY SUITS YER

D'YER THINK SO? THANKS, PET!

POOR LITTLE DEVIL, 'E TRIES! —I DIDN'T 'AVE THE HEART T' TELL 'IM I JUST WENT TO MAKE AN APPOINTMENT
Smythe

AH-AHH! SO AT LAST I'VE CAUGHT—
RENT

RENT

Smythe
—YOU IN

LOOK, MATE, WOULDN'T YER SAY THAT FIFTEEN TRIPS T' THE BAR WAS ENOUGH AT YOUR AGE?

MEBBE YER RIGHT, PET – ME FEET *ARE* KILLIN' ME

SHE'S A LOVELY LASS!
Smythe

THERE'S ANDY OVER THERE – I'LL POP OVER AN' 'AVE A WORD WITH 'IM

1

HI' THERE, ANDY – 'AVE YER KISSED THE BRIDE ?

2

3

4

IT'S FLIPPIN' DEPRESSIN'. NEVER GOT THE PRICE OF A PINT, OWING EVERYBODY MONEY — IF ONLY I COULD GET ON ME FEET AGAIN!
RAT-A-TAT TAT-TAT!

YER'VE GOT YER WISH, KID — THEY'RE COMIN' TO TAKE THE SOFA AWAY TOMORROW

ANDY'S BEEN ILL IN BED
THE LAST COUPLE OF DAYS,
RUBY - I'LL JUST POP OVER
AN' SEE
'OW 'E IS

'OW IS
'E?
GREAT - BUT FLO
ISN'T LOOKIN'
TOO GOOD

'E SHOULD 'AVE TAKEN ME OUT – TONIGHT OF ALL NIGHTS...!

D' YOU REALIZE IT WAS OUR WEDDIN' ANNIVERSARY TODAY?!

OF COURSE, I DO – I 'AD A COUPLE O' DRINKS T' CELEBRATE

I SUPPOSE THIS IS WHAT THEY CALL A 'NON-EVENT'

I THINK I'LL 'AVE ANOTHER ONE, PET
THAT'LL BE YER EIGHTH!

SEVENTH!

EIGHTH!

LOOK, I'VE GOT A SPLITTIN' 'EADACHE — T' SAVE AN ARGUMENT WE'LL START ALL OVER AGAIN
Smythe

HIC

1

YOO-HOO! IT'S LOVER BOY COMIN' UP FOR A KISS FROM 'IS LITTLE SWEET'EART!

2

3

I'VE NEVER 'AD MUCH TROUBLE GETTIN' 'ER OFF TO WORK ON TIME!
SMYTHE

4

LICENSED
BETTING OFFIC

TERRIBLE LUCK, PET – COULDN'T DO A THING RIGHT. STILL, THAT'S 'OW IT GOES, THERE'S ALWAYS TOMORROW

THERE'S THIS ABOUT IT, KID – I'VE STILL GOT THE ONE THING THAT MONEY CAN'T BUY
YOU 'AVE?

YEAH, POVERTY!
Smythe

YER'VE NEVER CARED TWO HOOTS ABOUT ME!

WHO GETS UP IN THE MIDDLE OF THE NIGHT WHEN YER COME 'OME FIGHTIN' DRUNK?!

EVERYBODY IN THE FLIPPIN' STREET!!

OH, MRS. CAPP, THERE'S SOMETHIN' YOU OUGHT TO KNOW...
1

I DON'T WANT T' CAUSE ANY TROUBLE, BUT LAS'NIGHT ANDY SAID THAT 'E WAS IN LOVE WITH ME
2

THAT'S ALL RIGHT, PET – WHY SHOULD 'E MAKE YOU THE EXCEPTION?

3

SILLY CAT
Smythe

4

LOOK, MATE, WHEN I WANT T' BE SAVED I'LL GIVE YOU A SHOUT -PUT ME DOWN.!

I'M LATE FOR WORK, RUBE! WOULD YER ATTEND TO ANDY F' ME?!
OKAY, PET

BREAKFAST COMIN' UP!

THANKS, FLO

SHE'S RIGHT, Y'KNOW – 'E LIVES IN A WORLD OF 'IS OWN!
Smythe

'OW'S 'E TREATIN' YER THESE DAYS, FLORRIE?
'E GIVES ME EVERY PENNY 'E GETS

IT'S TRUE – 'E DOES

... MIND YOU, I NEVER GET A SNIFF OF THE NOTES AN' SILVER!
Smythe

HIC

THUMP

YEAR IN, YEAR OUT! -'OW CAN YER KEEP COMIN' 'OME T' ME IN A STATE LIKE THIS ?!

SIMPLE ARITHMETIC -YER GET UP ONCE OFTENER THAN YER FALL DOWN
Smythe

OH, BLIMEY! TRUST YOU TO START MENDIN' A LADDER IN YER STOCKIN' DEAD ON OPENIN' TIME!
1

YER WERE EVEN TWENTY MINUTES LATE FOR OUR WEDDIN' BECAUSE YER STOPPED T' MEND A LADDER IN ONE OF YER STOCKIN'S—
2

I'LL TELL YER THIS, ONE MINUTE MORE AN' I'D 'AVE WALKED OUT OF THAT REGISTRY OFFICE!
3

I WISH I'D STOPPED T' MEND THE OTHER ONE
Smythe
4

DECIDED WHERE YOU AN' THE MISSUS ARE OFF TO THIS YEAR, TOM?

YES, ANDY, DEVON AN' CORNWALL

-I'M GOIN' TO CORNWALL
MMM.. SHOULD BE NICE
Smythe

LABOUR
EXCHANGE

ENGINEERING
COMPANY
ANY EXPERIENCE IN DRILLING?

YES, SIR! I WAS A SERGEANT IN THE FUSILIERS!
CLICK

INEERING
MPANY
SLAM!

WHAT AM I GOIN' T' DO? I DON'T KNOW WHERE ME NEXT DOLLAR'S COMIN' FROM!

LOOK, WE'VE **ALL** GOT OUR PROBLEMS—

I DON'T KNOW WHERE 'ER LAST DOLLAR'S ***GOIN'*** TO!
RACING
TURF TIPS
DOG RACING
POOLS

RAT-A TAT-TAT!

GOOD MORNIN', SIR, I 'OPE I DIDN'T DISTURB YER

OH, NO, NOT AT ALL - I WAS JUST SITTIN' IN THE BATH WAITIN' FOR SOMEBODY T' KNOCK

BOP

NO NEED T' GET UP, PET

YER DON'T MIND IF I GET MESELF ANOTHER BEER, D'YER?

CONGRATULATIONS, ANDY! I KNEW YOU'D TURN OVER A NEW LEAF IF I NAGGED YOU LONG ENOUGH!

I HEARD ALL ABOUT YOU SINGING YOUR HEAD OFF AT CHOIR PRACTICE LAS'NIGHT – WELL DONE!
ANY TIME

SO *THAT'S* WHERE I WAS

'ERE GOES, CATCH 'IM AT THE RIGHT TIME...
1

OKAY IF I INVITE MOTHER OVER F' THE WEEKEND, PET?
A LONG DRAG AT 'ER AGE, ISN'T IT?
2

A LONG DRAG? – IT ONLY TAKES 'ER HALF AN HOUR T' GET 'ERE –
3

YEAH! AN' A FORTNIGHT T' GET BACK 'OME!
Smythe
4

THAT 'ORRIBLE BLOKE AT THE END OF THE BAR –'E SOUNDS A RIGHT LITTLE TROUBLE MAKER!

THAT'S ME 'USBAND

SORRY, MISSUS – MY MISTAKE

NO, MISSUS —MINE

LABOUR
EXCHANGE

I'M MISSUS CAPP, ME 'USBAND'S SENT ME TO DRAW 'IS MONEY
ANY PROOF OF IDENTITY? BANK BOOK, T.V. LICENCE OR SUCH?

NO
FINE

IF SHE COULD PRODUCE THOSE SORTA THINGS YER COULD BE SURE IT WASN'T 'ER!
Smythe

A FINE STATE YOU WERE IN WHEN YER CAME TO BED LAS'NIGHT!
ME?

YES, YOU!
I WASN'T, Y'KNOW

ALL RIGHT, YER WEREN'T
Smythe

I'VE DECIDED TO COME BACK AN' SHARE YER BURDENS
?

BURDENS? – I 'AVEN'T GOT ANY BURDENS!

YER WILL 'AVE – ME MOTHER'S FOLLOWIN' ON, SHE'S BEEN EVICTED

THERE MUST BE MORE T' LIVIN' THAN THIS - THERE *MUST* BE! THE SAME ROUTINE, DAY AFTER DAY -
SHADDUP! AN' GET T' SLEEP!
1

LIFE'S PASSIN' ME BY. IS THIS WHAT I WAS BORN FOR? — JUST GOIN' T' BED AN' GETTIN' UP?
2

3

4

GOOD F' YOU, FLO!
BOP!

YER MUST BE THE 'APPIEST WOMAN IN THE WORLD NOW YER KNOW 'OW TO LAY 'IM OUT
NO, RUBE-

I WAS THROWIN' SO MANY PUNCHES, I DON'T KNOW WHICH ONE DID IT!
TCH!

DID YER READ 'OW MUCH A BLOKE PAID FOR A PAINTING THE OTHER DAY, ANDY?
CHANGE THE SUBJECT, MATE —MONEY'S JUST TROUBLE T' ME

IT *IS* ?!
YEAH—

—I 'AVEN'T GOT ENOUGH OF IT!
HIRE PURCHASE
RENT

WE'LL SETTLE THIS OUTSIDE, MATE!
SUIT Y'SELF
RENT

PSST! COULD YER TELL ME A COUPLE OF 'IS WEAK POINTS, FLO?

YES, PERCY - BOOZE AN' BARMAIDS!
HEH! HEH!
HEH! HEH!
EVERYBODY'S A COMIC

BANK

TOMMY HASLAM-!

BEHIND EVERY SUCCESSFUL MAN THERE'S ALWAYS A BLOKE WHO WENT TO SCHOOL WITH 'IM!
Smythe

'ELLO THERE, BRENDA. STILL FANCY-FREE? I THOUGHT YER WOULD 'AVE GOT YERSELF MARRIED BY NOW
I'M THINKIN' ABOUT IT, AUNT FLORRIE. IT'S NOT MUCH FUN BEING ON YER OWN
1

- IT MUST BE NICE TO 'AVE SOMEBODY T' TALK TO
YES, DEAR
2

KIDS — YER CAN'T TELL THEM! SHE'LL LEARN
Z

EEK!

OH-OHH!
SCREECH

IF THERE'S ONE TIME A WORM'LL TURN, IT'S WHEN 'ER LINE FULL OF WASHIN' COMES DOWN IN THE MUD!
Smythe

I SHOULDN'T 'AVE T' BE TURNIN' OUT F' WORK ON MORNIN'S LIKE THIS!

YER SHOULD BE THANKFUL YER IN GOOD SHAPE, LASS! NOT LIKE SOME POOR WOMEN OF YOUR AGE–

LIKE ALICE, WITH 'ER IMAGINARY ILLNESSES AN' DELUSIONS

IT CAN'T BE ANY WORSE THAN THE FLIPPIN' REALITIES!
Smythe

HEY, FLO, YER'VE FORGOT YER UMBRELLA — I'LL GET IT
1

'E'S GOT A MARVELLOUS MEMORY, NEVER FORGETS A THING
2

3

4

I WISH OUR GARDEN LOOKED AS LOVELY AS YOURS, FLO — WHAT'S YER SECRET?

HEY, YOU! STOP YER YAPPIN' AN' LET 'ER GET ON WITH IT!

'E'S GOT A GREEN TONGUE!
Smythe

THIS CASE HANDLE ISN'T TOO STRONG, PET – IT'LL BE OFF BY THE TIME WE GET T' BLACKPOOL. I'LL GO AN' BORROW ERIC'S

TCH! I WAS GOIN' T' ASK 'IM F' THE LOAN OF 'IS SUITCASE.... **YOU** DON'T 'APPEN TO 'AVE ONE, D'YER?
WAH!

I'LL TAKE JUST SO MUCH NAGGIN' AN' NO MORE! —I'M ONLY HUMAN!

WHEN ANYBODY SAYS THAT, YER CAN BET YER BOOTS THEY'RE GOIN' TO DO SOMETHIN' INHUMAN!

YER RIGHT, PET, THERE'S NOTHIN' WORSE THAN A HUSBAND LEADIN' A DOUBLE LIFE

THERE *IS* Y'KNOW – A WIFE LEADIN' A *SINGLE* LIFE!

?
Smythe

1

2

THAT'S ALL RIGHT, KID - I'LL LOOK AFTER YER

3

ONE OF THE FIRST RULES IS NOT TO HOG THE WHOLE BAR

4

EMPLOYMENT
EXCHANGE

AH, YES. THERE'S A FACTORY HERE THAT REQUIRES A COUPLE OF NEW HANDS—

I'D BE NO GOOD FOR THAT, MATE — I'VE 'AD THIS PAIR FOR AGES!

EVERY ONE A WINNER
Smythe

THEY'VE GOT T' BE *KIDDIN'*!
RATE INCREASES

THEY'RE NOT GOIN' T' GET AWAY WI' THIS! – I'M OFF T' THE TOWN HALL!

WHAT 'AVE THEY RATED US AS, PET?

IDIOTS!

SHE'S DRIVIN' ME ROUND THE BEND. FLIPPIN' WOMEN! GIVE 'EM AN INCH AN' THEY'LL TAKE A YARD!

YER RIGHT, FRIEND, I COULDN'T AGREE MORE

BOP
THAT'S MY MISSUS YER TALKIN' ABOUT!

YER NEVER 'ERE WHEN I NEED YER – THAT NEW COLLECTOR TRIED T' GET FAMILIAR WITH ME AGAIN!

37
YEAH? WELL, YER'D BETTER GO AN' CLEAN ME PIGEON LOFT RIGHT AWAY
IS THAT GOIN' TO STOP 'IM?!
NO, BUT IT'LL GET THAT SMIRK OFF YER CLOCK

TCH! TCH! YOU WOULDN'T CATCH ME THROWING MY MONEY AWAY ON THE HORSES!
RACING

YER WOULDN'T CATCH ME THROWIN' MINE AWAY EITHER
LICENSE
BETTING
RACING

OH, NO!
Smythe

SPARKLING
ALES

BAR
SPAR
AL

SPARKLING
ALES

1

2

SHE'S GOT TO BE KIDDIN' –
3

THAT BLOKE'S IN BAD COMPANY EVEN WHEN 'E'S ON 'IS OWN!
RENT
Smythe
4

YOUNG FELLER AT THE END OF THE BAR SENT YER THIS WITH 'IS COMPLIMENTS, MISS

YER'D BE SURPRISED AT THE NUMBER OF MARRIAGES THIS PUB'S PRODUCED
REALLY, AUNT FLORRIE?

YES, PET- IT'S JUST ONE OF THOSE RISKS YOU 'AVE T' TAKE
HIC
RACING

WATCH IT, MATE, YER DON'T WANT T' THROW THIRTY YEARS OF MARRIAGE OVERBOARD, D'YER..?

THEN AGAIN, THERE WAS FIVE YEARS EXPERIENCE AS A BOY-FRIEND IT'D BE A PITY T' WASTE...

YER LOOK REAL TIRED, FLO — IS YER CLEANIN' JOB GETTIN' A BIT TOO MUCH FOR YER?
Z

YER CAN SAY THAT AGAIN, RUBE! BUT IT'S 'ARD TO FIND SOMETHIN' LIGHTER WHEN YER MY AGE AN' GOT NO SPECIAL TALENTS
Z

YER TOO MODEST, FLO. LOOK 'OW GOOD YER WERE AT ENGLISH WHEN WE WERE AT SCHOOL — WHAT USE 'AVE YOU EVER MADE OF THAT?
TALKED!

I'M A ONE-MAN WOMAN AN' 'E'S A ONE-WOMAN MAN...

RENT

....AN' ONCE A WEEK THE FOUR OF US GET TOGETHER FOR A GAME O' DOMINOES

FLIPPIN' MARVELLOUS! ME OFF TO WORK, AN' YOU LYIN' UP THERE IN BED ALL DAY!

THE HIGHER ALTITUDE'S GOOD F' ME ASTHMA – HEH! HEH! HEH!

I'VE YET TO MEET A WOMAN WITH A SENSE OF HUMOUR
SLAM!

NATTER
NATTER
NATTER

EEEK!!

I'LL 'AVE T' DO SOMETHIN' ABOUT ME NERVES, RUBY – THAT WAS JUST THE KETTLE AGAIN!
TCH! TCH!

ANDY, ON YER WAY T' THE DOLE WOULD YER BUY A GET-WELL CARD F' ME MOTHER AN' POP IT IN 'ER LETTER-BOX?
SURE, PET
1

ALES

SENTIMENT'S EASY — LET'S 'AVE SOME ACTION
3

-LIKE DRINKIN' TO 'ER HEALTH!
Smythe
4

HUH! IT WON'T LAST – D' **YOU** THINK BRAINY WOMEN MAKE GOOD WIVES, ANDY?

JUST ONCE, I'D LIKE TO TASTE A DRINK THAT YOU 'AD PAID FOR-!
BAR

YER THE MEANEST BLOKE I'VE EVER COME ACROSS —

BUS STOP
CANCEL THAT LAST REMARK

GRR! GRR!
WOULD YOU SAY I WAS TWO-FACED, FLO?

NEVER!

'E WOULDN'T BE WEARIN' THAT ONE IF 'E WAS! HEH!
Smythe

NATIONAL
ASSISTANCE
I DON'T CARE WHAT YER SAY, MATEY, SOMETHIN'S GOT T' BE DONE – WE CAN'T EXIST ON THIS –!

ATIONAL
SISTANCE
YOU BLOKES DON'T SEEM T' REALIZE –I'VE GOT FOURTEEN MOUTHS T' FEED!
?

PARDON ME FOR ASKIN' – BUT WHO'S THE OTHER TWELVE?

ME PIGEONS 'AVE TO EAT, DON'T THEY?!
Smythe

Smythe